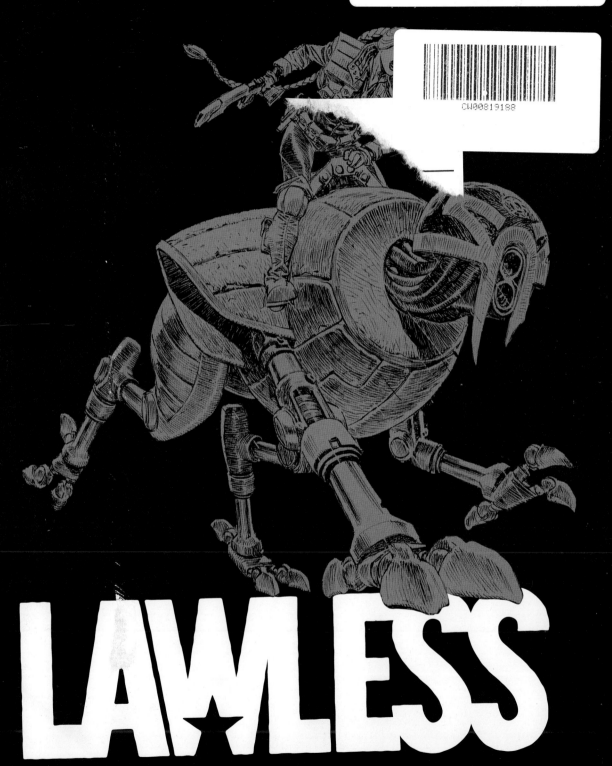

LAWLESS

ASHES TO ASHES

LAWLESS CREATED BY DAN ABNETT & PHIL WINSLADE

THE STORY SO FAR

COLONIAL MARSHAL, METTA LAWSON, is assigned to the frontier planet 43 Rega replacing disgraced and unstable psi-judge Hetch.

Reporting for duty in the town of Badrock, which acts as a hub for the mines and the corporate office of Munce Inc, the corporation behind much of the financial investment of Badrock, she meets her clerk, **NERYS PETTIFER**, an enthusiastic but inexperienced officer. Shortly after arrival she meets the 'uplifted' gorilla **KILL-A-MAN JAROO** and discovers that tensions between the Meks, Muties, Uplifts and humans are rife.

But when Metta Lawson decides to increase the peace, **ALDIS BROTHERLY**, the regional head of Munce Inc, finding her interventions disruptive becomes determined to stop her, resorting to hiring N.G.O. Enforcers to keep the status quo as he prefers it. Metta Lawson foils their plans and takes Aldis Brotherly into custody.

After this setback Munce Inc, under their new 'asset manager', **TEXANNA PINCHER**, decide that Badrock is a liability and proceed to attempt to wipe the town from the face of the planet, and Metta Lawson with it, initially through subterfuge, but then more blatantly with aerial bombardment.

All these attempts are stopped by Metta Lawson, who has banded together the recently freed Muties, Meks, Humans and Uplifted Gorillas into a force that is determined to halt Munce Inc's plans. We last saw Metta Lawson preparing to defend Badrock against a more direct assault by Texanna Pincher and her amassed forces of Munce Inc.

ASHES TO ASHES

Script: Dan Abnett
Art: Phil Winslade
Letters: Ellie de Ville

Originally published in *Judge Dredd Megazine* 400-409

GETTING AWFUL DARK OVER WILL'S MOTHER...

IT'S *WHAT?*

GETTING AWFUL D—

NEVER MIND. JUST SOMETHING MY AUNTIE USED TO SAY.

WHEN THE SKY GOT DARK. BEFORE A STORM.

'GETTING AWFUL DARK OVER WILL'S MOTHER,' SHE'D SAY.

WHO IS 'WILL'?

I DON'T KNOW, KILL-A-MAN. DON'T THINK MY *AUNTIE* KNEW EITHER. NOT WILL, NOR HIS MOTHER.

JUST A *MADE-UP SAYING.* YOU KNOW HOW FOLK GET WHEN THEY'RE *OLD.*

I *DO NOT.* I AM *NOT* OLD.

NOT LIKELY TO *GET OLD,* NEITHER.

SHITSTICKS, RONDO! YOU ARE A DROKKIN' *TOWER* OF POSITIVITY!

SORRY.

I'M GOING TO CALL YOU *'THE CHEER-LEADER'.* BECAUSE IRONY.

PLEASE DON'T.

RONDO THE *CHEER-LEADER.* WE CAN GIT YOU SOME OF THEM *POM-POMS* AND AN 'ITTLE-BITTY *KICKY SKIRT.*

I WOULD PAY *ACTUAL MONEY* TO SEE THAT.

WHY ARE YOU *LAUGHING?* NONE OF THIS IS FUNNY!

RONDO, WE'RE LAUGHING AT YOU *BECAUSE* NONE OF THIS IS FUNNY.

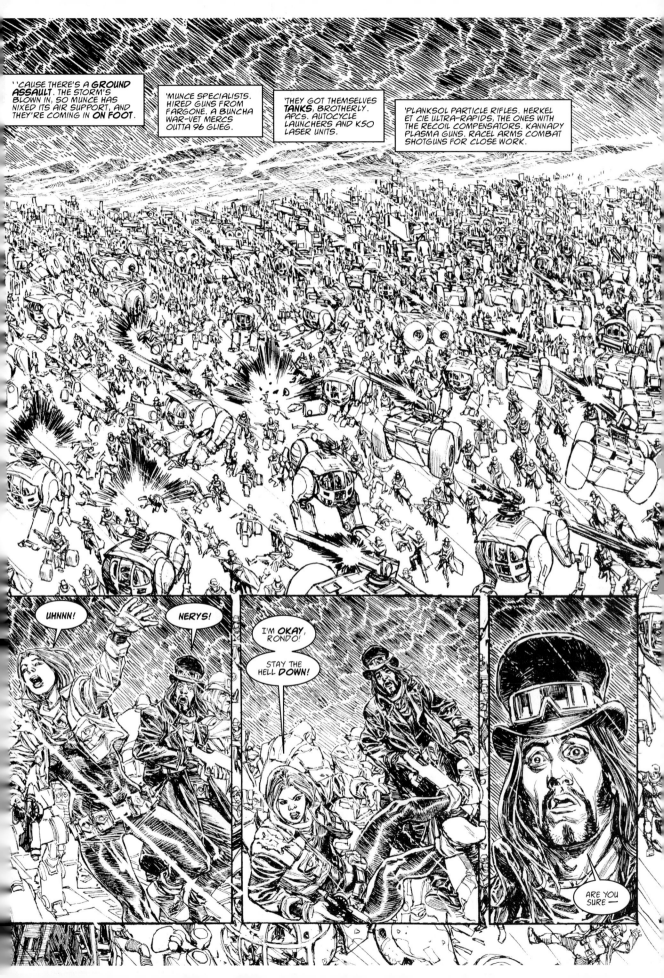

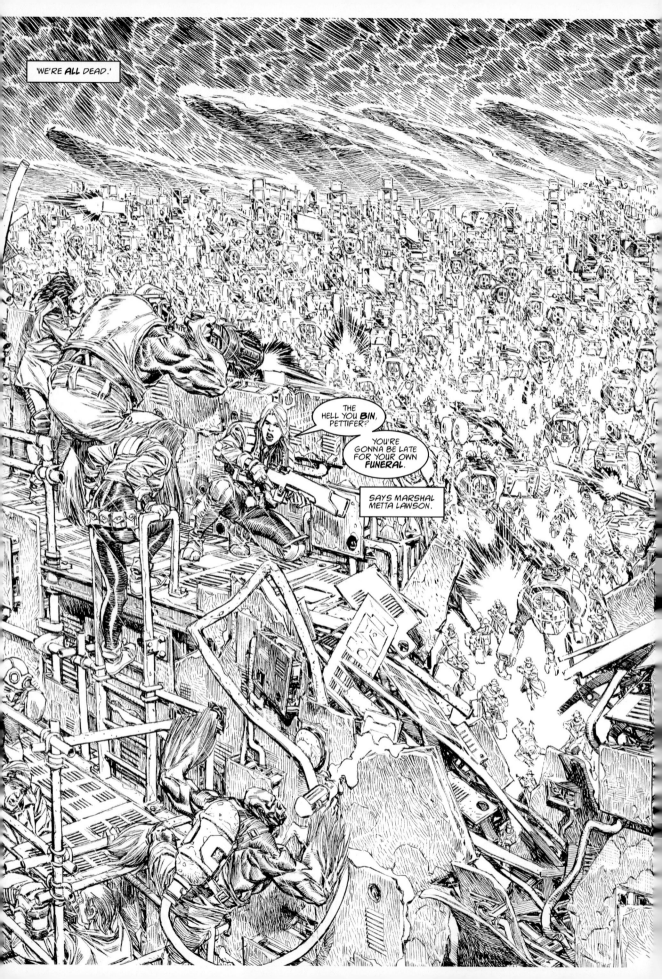

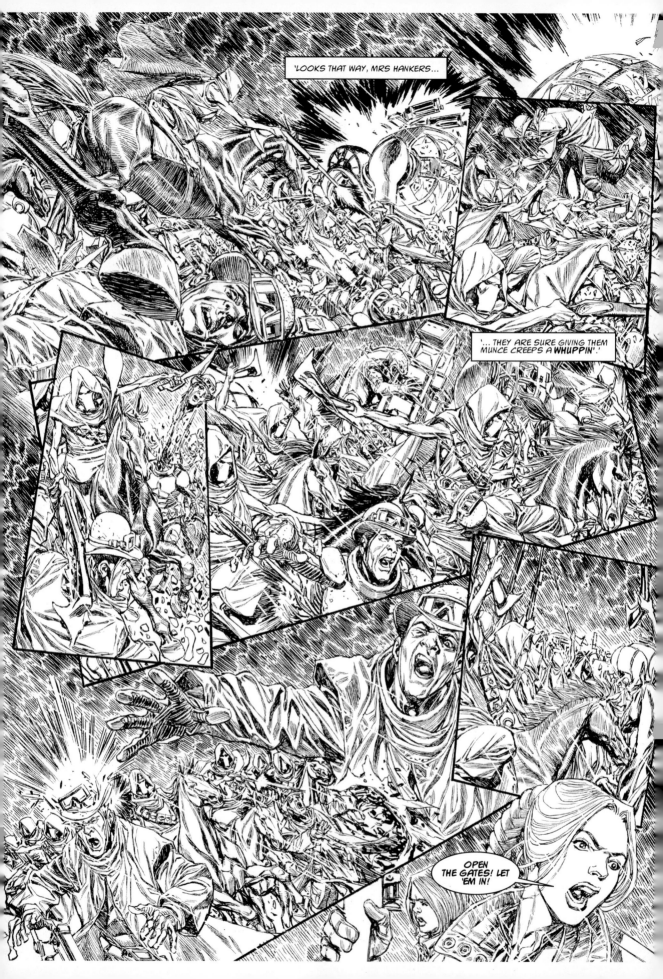

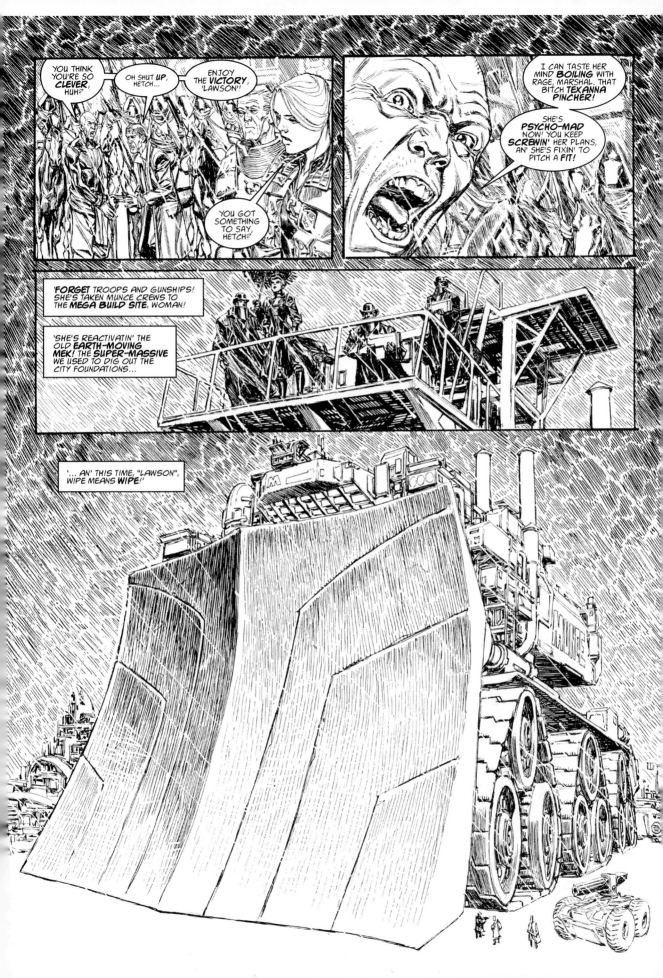

I KNOW THAT MEK FROM THE MEGA-BUILD, MARSHAL.

THERE'S NOT A **THING** IN THIS TOWN THAT WILL EVEN MAKE A **DENT** IN IT.

SO **WHAT?** DO WE... TAKE OUR CHANCES AND **RUN?**

DROKK **THAT** TO HELL. IF WE DO, WHAT WAS THE POINT OF **ANY** OF THIS?

WE JUST LEAVE OUR **PRINCIPLES** HERE TO GET SQUASHED?

'SIDES... RUN TO **WHERE?** THE **RADLANDS** OR THE **RADLANDS?** HOW LONG WOULD WE **LAST?**

ER, I THINK I MAY KNOW HOW TO STOP IT.

A BIG MEK LIKE THAT, I THINK I MIGHT KNOW H—

DROKK, O' **COURSE** YOU DO! THE EARTH-MOVER IS **MUNCE TECH.** YOU'VE GOT CODES TO **CONTROL** THAT STUFF, **DON'T** YOU, BROTHERLY?

NO, LAWSON. THAT'S NOT WHAT I'M SUGGESTING.

TEXANNA PINCHER WILL HAVE **OVER-WRITTEN** MY CODES **LONG** SINCE.

SO **WHAT,** BROTHERLY?

I RECALL THIS TIME ON 72 ORDINE, A BIG MUNCE MEK ON THE MEGA-BUILD THERE WENT **HAYWIRE.**

THE UPLIFT CREW STOPPED IT WITH AN **EM PULSE.**

FRIED ITS **BRAIN** AND STOPPED IT **DEAD.**

YOU KNOW? **THAT'S** A THING.

BACK IN THE WAR, SJS USED THAT TACTIC **PLENTY** AGAINST MEK UNITS.

ELECTRO-MAG BURSTS. IT **WORKS.**

I CAN DO IT, MARSHAL.

LORD GRUD WILLING, IN **FIFTEEN** MINUTES.

THANK **YOU,** GEES-S!

SHIT. OKAY.

QUESTION IS, CAN WE **FANGLE UP** AN E-MAG BOMB IN TIME?

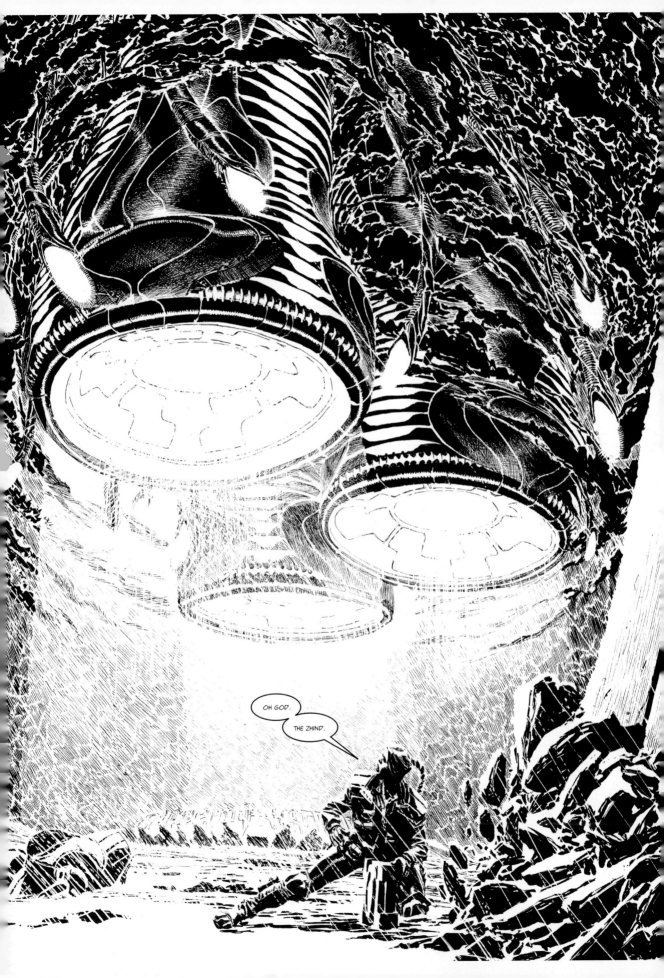

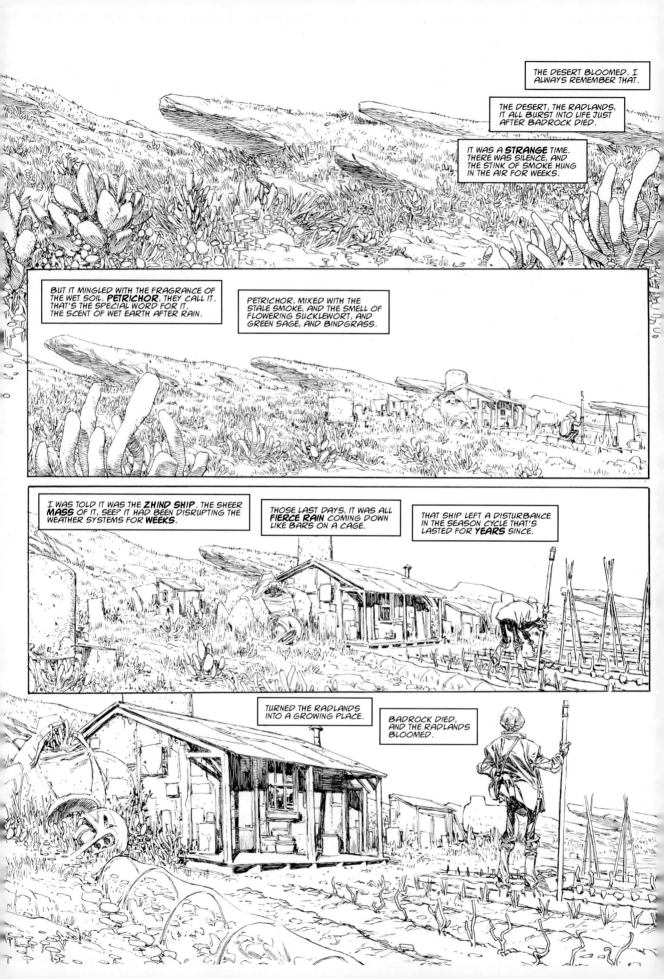

THE DESERT BLOOMED. I ALWAYS REMEMBER THAT.

THE DESERT, THE RADLANDS, IT ALL BURST INTO LIFE JUST AFTER BADROCK DIED.

IT WAS A **STRANGE** TIME. THERE WAS SILENCE, AND THE STINK OF SMOKE HUNG IN THE AIR FOR WEEKS.

BUT IT MINGLED WITH THE FRAGRANCE OF THE WET SOIL. **PETRICHOR**, THEY CALL IT. THAT'S THE SPECIAL WORD FOR IT. THE SCENT OF WET EARTH AFTER RAIN.

PETRICHOR, MIXED WITH THE STALE SMOKE, AND THE SMELL OF FLOWERING SUCKLEWORT, AND GREEN SAGE, AND BINDGRASS.

I WAS TOLD IT WAS THE **ZHIND SHIP**. THE SHEER **MASS** OF IT, SEE? IT HAD BEEN DISRUPTING THE WEATHER SYSTEMS FOR **WEEKS**.

THOSE LAST DAYS, IT WAS ALL **FIERCE RAIN** COMING DOWN LIKE BARS ON A CAGE.

THAT SHIP LEFT A DISTURBANCE IN THE SEASON CYCLE THAT'S LASTED FOR **YEARS** SINCE.

TURNED THE RADLANDS INTO A GROWING PLACE.

BADROCK DIED, AND THE RADLANDS BLOOMED.

BADROCK DIED, BUT I LIVED.

SOMEHOW.

AND I HAVE **LIVED ON** HERE.

IT'S NOT MUCH OF A LIVING, BUT I HAVE NOWHERE ELSE TO GO.

AND 'SIDES, I HAVE **RESPONSIBILITIES** HERE.

I LOOK AFTER THE FOLK OF BEDROCK. WATCH OVER THEM, LIKE I **ALWAYS** DID.

NERYS PETTIFER

ROYAL WILTY

KILL A MAN

MUNCE WON, **INEVITABLY**.

TEXANNA PINCHER AND HER HIRED GUNS AND THAT SUPERMASSIVE MEK FROM THE BUILD SITE.

UNVIABLE ASSET DISPOSAL, THEY CALLED IT.

YOU CAN STILL SEE THE TRACKS OF IT, EVEN **NOW**, FORTY YEARS ON. SCARS IN THE LAND.

SOMETIMES I FOLLOW THEM OUT TO THE MEGA-BUILD, JUST TO LOOK-SEE.

AND I REMEMBER OLD HETCH'S DREAMS OF BODIES IN THE DIRT. A MASS GRAVE. BONES IN THE DUST.

AND HE WAS **RIGHT**.

'COURSE, **HE** DIED TOO. ALONG WITH THEM ALL.

MY BONES SHOULD BE WITH THEM.

BUT I GOT TO LIVE.

SOMEHOW.

I GOT TO SEE THE LONG AFTERWARDS. THE DESERT BLOOMING. THE GREEN SAGE AND THE SUCKLEWORT. THE TURN OF THE YEARS.

THE MEGA-BUILD, NEVER FINISHED, FALLING TO RUIN. A CITY THAT NEVER WAS.

AND THEN THE **WAR**.

THE ARRIVAL OF THE ZHIND SHIP ALERTED THE AUTHORITIES IN THE PLANETARY CAPITAL.

THEY ARRIVED TOO **LATE** TO SAVE BADROCK FROM MUNCE, OF COURSE, BUT THAT WASN'T THEIR CONCERN **ANYWAY**.

THE ZHIND WERE BACK. WE'D FOUGHT **ONE** WAR AGAINST THEM AND NOW WE WERE FACING **ANOTHER**.

IT'S BEEN RAGING EVER SINCE. WORST CONFLICT IN OUR SPECIES' HISTORY.

IT'S GOING **BADLY**. BACK ON EARTH, THE BIG MEG IS ON THE EDGE OF CATASTROPHIC FINANCIAL COLLAPSE.

MAN'S GOING TO CRASH BACK INTO A **DARK AGE**, AND ALL THE DREAMS WE HAD OF EXPANSION AND SETTLEMENT ARE LOST.

OUT HERE, IT'S QUIET. **43** REGA IS A **SACRED** WORLD TO THE ZHIND, SO THE MEG FORCES FORTIFIED IT.

THE ONLY NEW THING I CAN SEE FROM MY WINDOW IS THE SJS FORTRESS YONDER.

ONE OF **EIGHTEEN** ON REGA.

I GOT A LITTLE PLACE ON WHAT USED TO BE HAZMAT SLOPE.

I MIND MY OWN, AND THE SPECIALS DON'T BOTHER ME.

MUCH.

I DON'T CATCH A WINK, NOT AFTER DRURY'S NEWS YESTERDAY.

SOMETIME IN THE SMALL HOURS, SITTING IN MY CHAIR, MY STUBBORN STREAK JUST SLOUGHED OFF ME LIKE OLD SKIN.

TO THINK, I WAS JUST GOING TO DIG IN AND RESIST. THE OLD BITCH WHO REFUSES TO BUDGE.

BUT NO. THERE'S A BETTER WAY TO RESIST.

TO DO SOMETHING THAT COUNTS. AFTER ALL THIS TIME.

OH, CATT. YOU'RE TOO FAR GONE FOR THIS RIDE...

RONDO   TINKERTON   NERYS PETTIFER

'COURSE, IT'LL MEAN LEAVING MY FRIENDS BEHIND. BUT THEY SAT UP WITH ME LAST NIGHT, AND WE SAID OUR GOOD-BYES. THEY UNDERSTAND I HAVE TO DO THIS.

CARRY A WARNING. TO WHOM IT MAY CONCERN.

SO I GET UP, SUN-PROOF MYSELF IN HAZ-GEAR, AND GATHER SOME KIT.

WATER, MOSTLY. IT'LL BE A LONG RIDE.

THEY GIVE ME WATER. ELECTROLYTES.

CALL ME BY MY NAME. MY **OLD** NAME.

TAKE ME SOMEWHERE.

HOLY GRUD...

THE ZHIND SHIP.

THE ONE THAT CAME TO BADROCK.

THE SJS BROUGHT IT DOWN IN THE FIRST PHASE OF THE WAR, **YEARS** BACK.

THIS IS WHERE IT WOUND UP. OUT **HERE**.

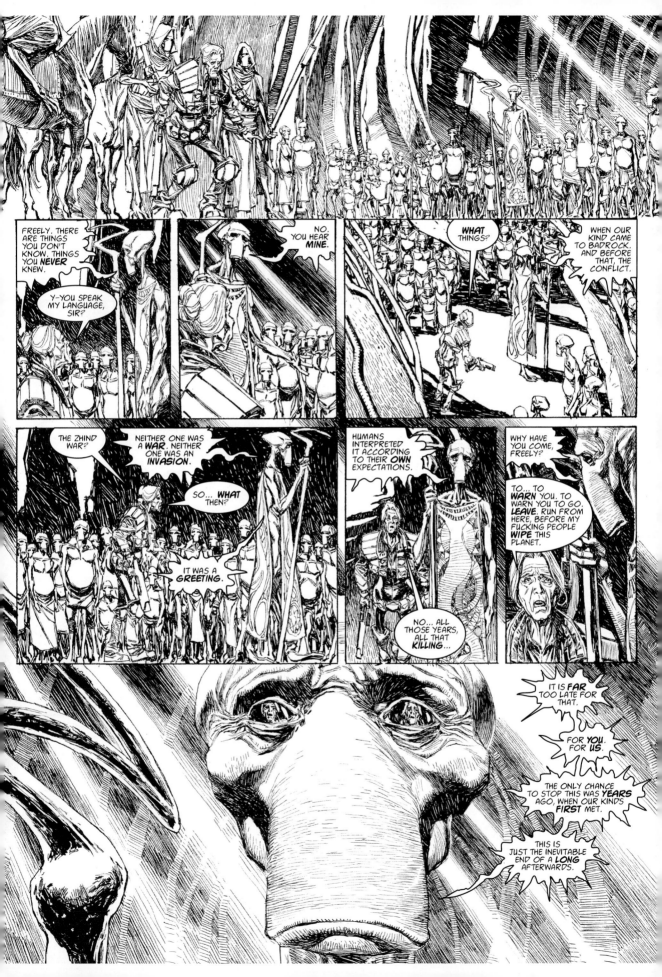

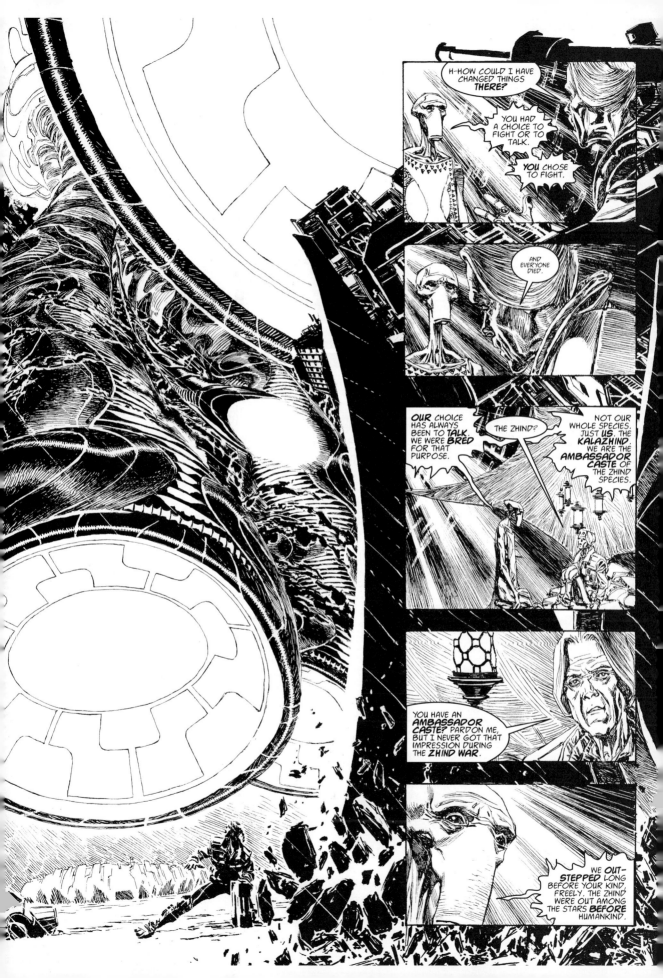

'WE WATCHED YOUR WORLD DEVELOP. BEFORE YOUR ATOMIC CONFLAGRATIONS, BEFORE THE RISE OF YOUR MEGA-CITIES, WE MADE MANY ATTEMPTS TO CONTACT YOU.

'WE LIKED YOU. WE ADMIRED YOU.

'WE KALAZHIND WERE SENT TO BROKER FRIENDSHIP.

'BUT THESE EFFORTS FAILED. THESE WERE THE FIRST MOMENTS LOST.

'WE WERE STARTLED BY HUMAN-KIND'S SELFISHNESS, GREED AND LACK OF SPECIES EMPATHY.

'EARTH WAS THEN DETERMINED TO BE DANGEROUS, AND LISTED AS OFF-LIMITS.

'THE KALAZHIND CASTE OF TELEPATHS WERE TRAUMATISED BY THOSE CONTACT ATTEMPTS.

'WE WERE RETIRED TO A SANCTUARY, WHERE WE COULD LIVE OUT OUR DAMAGED LIVES IN PEACE.'

HERE... 43 REGA.

BADROCK?

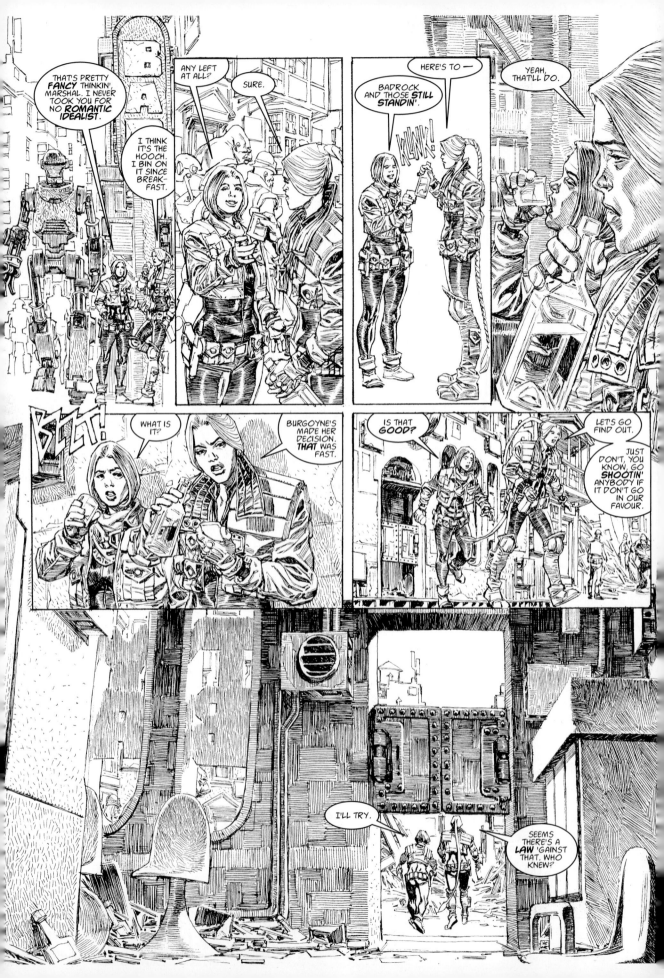

COME TO THE FREETOWN OF
BADROCK
INCORPORATED FREE TRADE SETTLEMENT ZONE
... THERE.
THAT'S PERFECT.
AT LAST.
WE'RE A FREE TOWN NOW? OFFICIALLY?
YEP. ALL CHARTERED AND MANDATED. DESIGNATED A FREE-TRADE AREA BY THE HALL OF JUSTICE, NO LESS.
TRIAL BASIS, NATURALLY, BUT I HAVE HIGH HOPES.
THE FUTURE, RON-DO. DON'T IT MAKE YOUR HEART SING?
I TRULY CAN'T TELL, MARSHAL. MINE'S MADE OF PLASTIC AND USED TA BELONG TO SOMEONE ELSE.

YOU HEALIN' OKAY?

SURE, DANDY.

SO THIS IS THE **NEW** BADROCK, HUH? THE GREAT **LIBERTARIAN EXPERIMENT**, WITH **YOU** IN CHARGE?

YOU... AND THE **SJS**?

HNH. THEY CAME AS PART OF THE DEAL... ADVISORY ROLE **ONLY**.

I NEVER MET FOUR MORE **UNSMILING, HUMOURLESS SONS** OF DROKKERS —

'CEPT DRURY. **HE'S** OKAY.

ONLY BY COMPARISON.

YOU SAID HE WAS KINDA CUTE —

BY **COMPARISON,** NERYS.

BUT I WILL SOON WHIP OUR SJS COLLEAGUES INTO SHAPE WITH MY **CHARM** AND **SPARKLIN'** PERSONALITY.

YEESH, GOOD LUCK WITH **THAT**...

I'M GUESSING **ROY** AIN'T TOO PLEASED ABOUT THEM BEING HERE?

YEAH, I THINK ROY WILL SOON BE SHIPPING OUT.

GOTTA MEET HIM IN THE SALOON IN A WHILE.

WE HAVE A **SALOON** AGAIN?

YUP. UNDER NEW MANAGEMENT. **MS BETHANY BITONI** —

SHE IS A **MALE IMPERSONATOR,** RONDO! CALLS HERSELF 'TONY DANCER' —

OR IS IT 'HISSELF'?

SHE —

—**WHAT** NOW?

NEVER MIND. YOU'LL CATCH UP SOON ENOUGH.

EVERYTHING'S **NEW,** RONDO! THAT'S THE **POINT!**

YEAH, SPEAKING OF NEW, **THAT'S** HARD TO MISS...

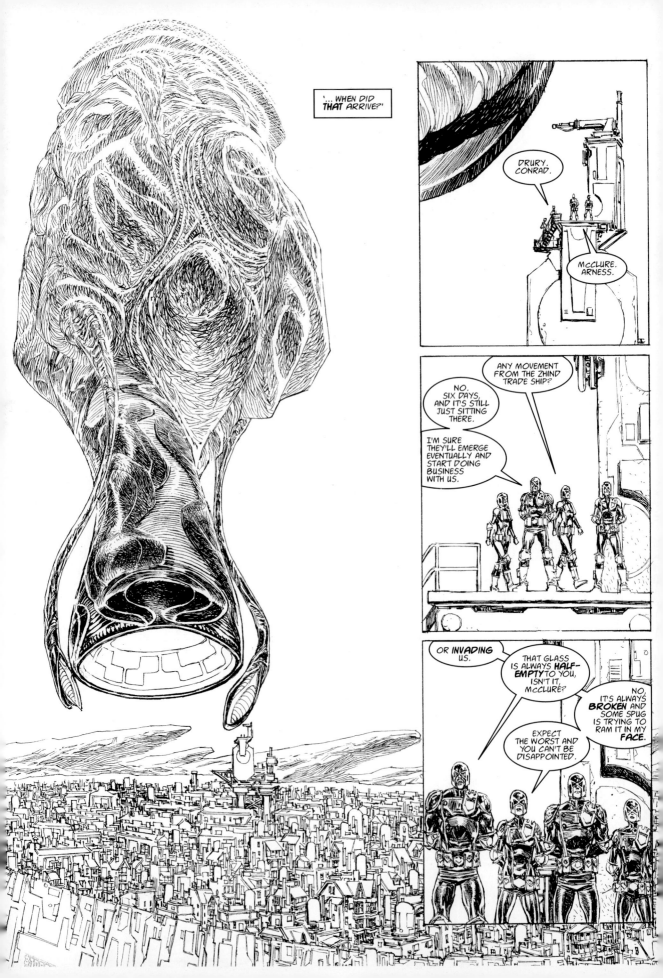

'... WHEN DID **THAT** ARRIVE?'

DRURY.
CONRAD.

McCLURE.
ARNESS.

ANY MOVEMENT FROM THE ZHIND TRADE SHIP?

NO. SIX DAYS, AND IT'S STILL JUST SITTING THERE.

I'M SURE THEY'LL EMERGE EVENTUALLY AND START DOING BUSINESS WITH US.

OR **INVADING** US.

THAT GLASS IS ALWAYS **HALF-EMPTY** TO YOU, ISN'T IT, McCLURE?

NO, IT'S ALWAYS **BROKEN** AND SOME SPUG IS TRYING TO RAM IT IN MY **FACE.**

EXPECT THE WORST AND YOU CAN'T BE DISAPPOINTED.

GALLERY

VIRAL

BRINK BOOK ONE
978-1-78108-550-9
£12.99

BRINK BOOK FOUR
978-1-78108-939-2
£12.99
Arriving: November 2021

BRINK BOOK TWO
978-1-78108-628-5
£12.99

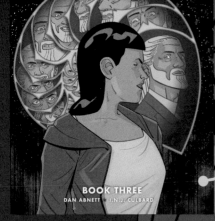

BRINK BOOK THREE
978-1-78108-676-6
£12.99

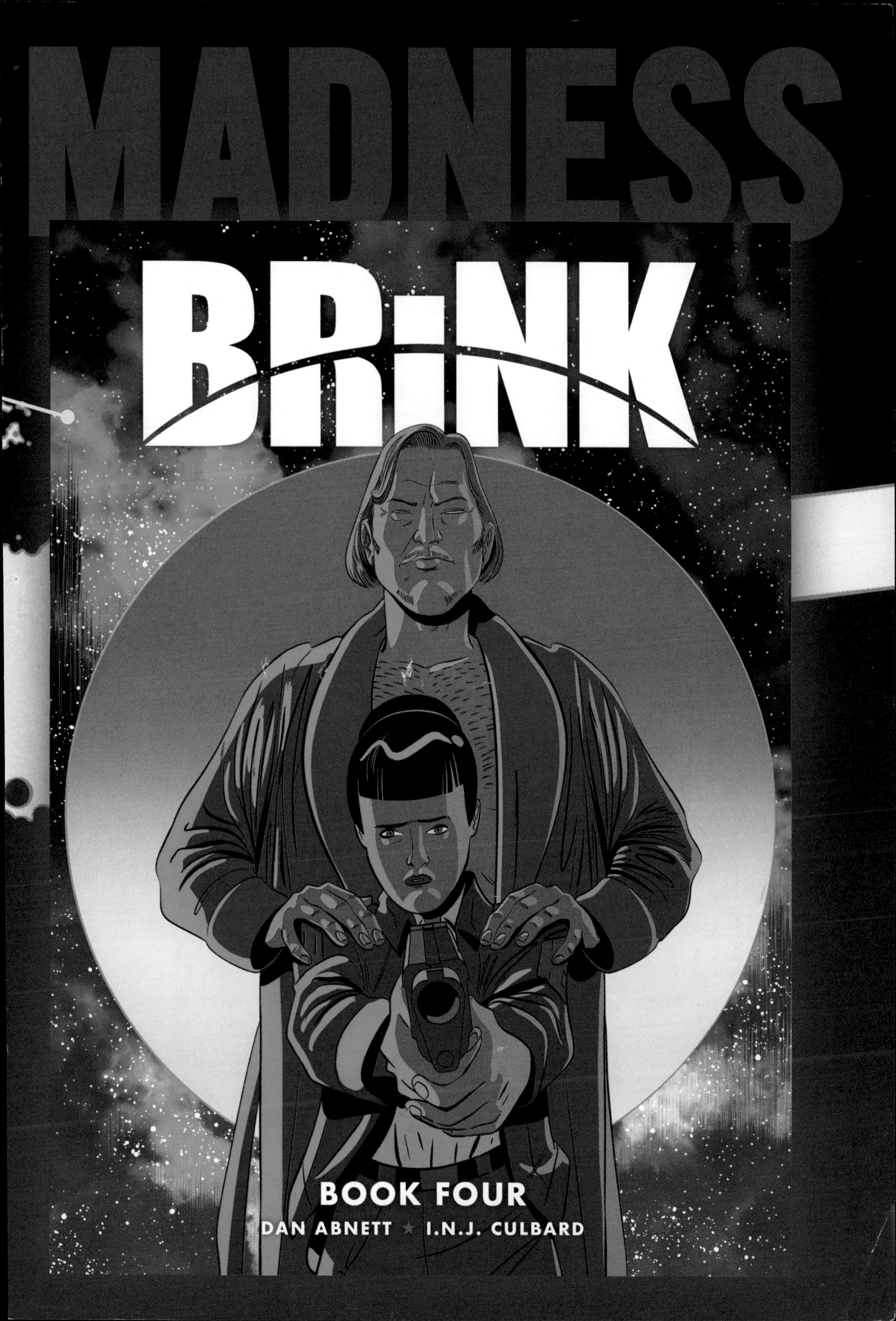
MADNESS
BRINK
BOOK FOUR
DAN ABNETT ★ I.N.J. CULBARD

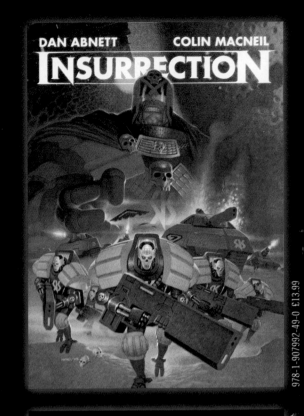